BATS
of the
United States

By

Michael J. Harvey
Tennessee Technological University

J. Scott Altenbach
University of New Mexico

Troy L. Best
Auburn University

Published by the
Arkansas Game & Fish Commission

In Cooperation with the
Asheville Field Office
U.S. Fish and Wildlife Service

1999

This publication was prepared for non-profit distribution.

Foreword

The Arkansas Game & Fish Commission is pleased to present *Bats of the United States*. For almost 15 years, the Commission has taken an active role in developing and publishing a series of booklets designed to increase appreciation of one of the most maligned and misunderstood groups of animals in the world. In 1986, we published *Arkansas Bats: A Valuable Resource*. This was followed in 1992, with *Bats of the Eastern United States*. With the publication of this book, we have expanded coverage to include all bats currently occurring in the United States. The primary goal of each publication has been to provide the citizens of Arkansas and the rest of the country with an accurate, well-written source of information on the life history and conservation needs of this intriguing group of animals. The first two publications were written by Dr. Michael J. Harvey, Tennessee Technological University. Dr. Harvey has spent much of his life learning about bat distribution, biology, and conservation. Although he has worked throughout the eastern United States, Dr. Harvey has devoted a significant portion of his career to the bats of Arkansas. These efforts have provided us with a much better understanding and appreciation of our endangered bats. Dr. Harvey is again the primary author of this publication. In this more wide ranging booklet, he is joined by two additional researchers who also have dedicated their careers to bats and their conservation. Dr. Troy L. Best, Auburn University, has done extensive research on the bats of the southeastern and southwestern United States, and Dr. J. Scott Altenbach, University of New Mexico-Albuquerque, has worked for many years to learn more about the bats of the western United States. In addition to his valuable conservation work, Dr. Altenbach is one of the world's best bat photographers. We are especially pleased that he is sharing his marvelous photographs with us in this new book.

The bats of the United States have suffered tremendous declines in recent years. In most cases, these declines are the direct result of human activities. We believe this book provides the information needed to convince the public that we must reverse these declines and thereby preserve this amazing group of animals for the enjoyment and benefit of future generations. Please join us in learning more about bats. I believe you will enjoy this beautiful, carefully crafted, and interesting publication as much as I have.

Steve N. Wilson

Steve N. Wilson, Director
Arkansas Game & Fish Commission

Acknowledgments

We thank our respective universities (MJH, Tennessee Technological University; JSA, University of New Mexico; TLB, Auburn University) for their aid in making this publication possible. Robert R. Currie, U.S. Fish and Wildlife Service, and Keith B. Sutton, Arkansas Game and Fish Commission, were especially helpful in arranging for funding from their agencies and in numerous other ways. Sutton served as project editor and coordinator. In addition to recognition for this effort, we express our appreciation to the Asheville Field Office, U.S. Fish and Wildlife Service, for their long-standing and continuing commitment to protection of the bats of the United States.

Because of the general nature of this publication, and due to the limited space available, we have not cited or referenced those numerous authors and publications from which we obtained much of the information presented in the individual species accounts. To those many scientists, we owe a deep debt of gratitude. Without the use of their published research results, this publication would not have been possible.

All bat photographs were provided by author J. Scott Altenbach. They represent a lifetime of bat research and photography. We sincerely thank those numerous individuals who aided in obtaining specimens to be photographed and/or who aided in other ways.

Finally, our sincere thanks to our families for their tolerance, patience, understanding, and support during our numerous nocturnal forays into the world of bats.

BATS
of the
United States

Michael J. Harvey
J. Scott Altenbach
Troy L. Best

Introduction

Bats may be the most misunderstood animals in the United States, although as consumers of enormous numbers of insects, they rank among the most beneficial.

Bats suffer from a bad public image in much of the world; misconceptions and superstitions about them are numerous. They are considered symbols of doom and darkness, close associates of Count Dracula, and various parts of their anatomies are used as magical ingredients in witches' brews ("eye of newt and toe of frog, wool of bat and tongue of dog").

Many people think bats are blind, fly like "bats out of hell," try to become entangled in human hair, are dirty and dangerous, are flying mice ("Die Fledermaus" to the Germans), and otherwise do things that drive people "batty" or cause them to have "bats in their belfries." Being referred to as an "old bat" or "dingbat" is less than complimentary. The book and movie "Nightwing" certainly didn't help bats' image. Actually, most bats are highly beneficial, intelligent, extremely interesting, and possess fascinating abilities such as homing instinct and the ability to navigate by echolocation in complete darkness.

Bats are highly regarded in some societies. In China, the word for bat is *fu*; the same word also means happiness or good luck. In Chinese art and handicraft, bats frequently are used to symbolize happiness. A favorite Chinese design is the *wu-fu*, which consists of a disk enclosing the symbol of life (a tree with roots and branches) and surrounded by five bats with spread wings facing inward. The bats symbolize the five great happinesses sought by all men—health, wealth, long life, good luck, and tranquility. The *wu-fu* symbol was chosen as the logo of Bat Conservation International, an organization whose purpose is to prevent extinction of bats, to ensure survival of viable bat populations, and to inform the public of the value of bats.

Although this publication focuses on bats of the United States, it contains information, including range maps, about all 21 species of bats found in Canada, because all Canadian species are present in both Canada and the United States.

Bat Biology

Bats, like humans, are mammals, having hair and giving birth to living young and feeding them on milk from mammary glands. Over 900 species of bats occur worldwide; they are most abundant in the tropics. Bats are second only to rodents in numbers among mammals and comprise about one-fifth of all mammal species. Forty-five bat species, representing four families and 19 genera, are native to the United States.

Worldwide, bats vary in size from only slightly over 2 grams (0.07 ounce—about the weight of a dime) to more than 1.5 kilograms (more than 3 pounds). The large "flying foxes" of Africa, Asia, Australia, and many Pacific islands may have a wingspan up to 2 meters (6 feet). United States bats vary in size from less than 3 grams (0.11 ounce) to 70 grams (2.5 ounces). The largest United States bat, the greater mastiff bat occurring from central California south into Mexico, has a wingspan of approximately 55 centimeters (22 inches).

Bats are the only true flying mammals, and their maneuverability while capturing insects on the wing is astonishing. Bats belong to the mammalian order Chiroptera, which means "hand-wing." The bones present in a bat's wing are the same as those of the human arm and hand, but bat finger bones are greatly elongated and connected by a double membrane of skin to form the wing. The oldest known fossil bats, from Wyoming and Europe, date back approximately 50 million years.

Bats primarily are nocturnal, although many fly early in the evening, sometimes before sunset. Occasionally, especially on warm winter days, they are observed flying during daylight hours.

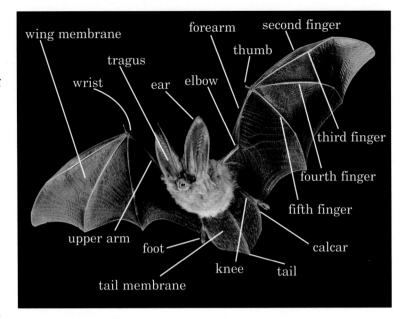

Echolocation

Although bats have relatively good eyesight, most depend on their superbly developed echolocation system (or sonar) to navigate and capture insects in the dark. Bats emit pulses of very high-frequency sound (inaudible to human ears) at a rate of a few to 200 per second. By listening to the echoes reflected back to them, they can discern objects in their path. Their echolocation ability is so acute they can avoid obstacles no wider than a piece of thread and capture tiny flying insects, even in complete darkness. This fantastic ability has been described as "seeing with their ears." Most larger

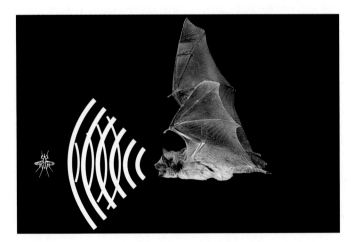

Bats Are Beneficial

Almost all United States bats, and 70 percent of bat species worldwide, feed almost exclusively on insects and are thus extremely beneficial. In fact, bats are the only major predators of night-flying insects.

Bats typically eat more than 50 percent of their body weight in insects each night, and a nursing female may consume enough insects to equal her own body weight, as many as 4,500 or more small insects. Thus, a summer colony of 1,000 bats weighing 10 grams each could consume 10 kilograms (22 pounds) of insects each night, or as many as 4,500,000 insects.

As an example, people in the Chattanooga, Tennessee, area benefit by having over 200,000 kilograms (more than 220 tons or 440,000 pounds) of insects removed from their area yearly by a colony of 200,000 gray bats that spends the summer in a cave near that city. Imagine 440 half-ton pickup trucks loaded to capacity with insects; that's a whole lot of bugs. Most residents of the area probably are unaware of the presence of their furry flying friends and how they benefit from the bats' presence. Bats provide similar benefits as natural insecticides throughout the nation and world. The amount of insects consumed by the hundreds of millions of bats is staggering.

Unfortunately, far too many people still believe the only good bat is a dead bat. It took many long years to educate people to the fact that hawks and other birds of prey are beneficial and should not be shot on sight. Hopefully, it will not take so long to educate the public about the true nature of bats and their importance in the ecosystem.

*Pallid bat (**Antrozous pallidus**) with a 13-lined June beetle captured on the wing.*

*Long-legged bat (**Myotis volans**) drinking from a quiet pool.*

Feeding Behavior

While insect-eating bats may capture flying insects in their mouths, they often capture insects on the wing by scooping them into their tail or wing membranes. They then reach down and take the insect into their mouth. This results in the erratic flight most people are familiar with when they observe bats feeding in the late evening or around lights at night. Bats drink by skimming close to the surface of a body of water and gulping an occasional mouthful. As seen on the back cover, Townsend's big-eared bat drinks with its tongue and keeps its body well above the water.

Non-insect Eating Bats

While most United States bat species are insectivorous, bats in other parts of the world feed on a variety of items in addition to insects. Many species, including the large "flying foxes," feed primarily on fruit, while several types feed on nectar and pollen. Much of the fruit consumed by fruit-eating species is overly ripe, and thus not a problem for fruit growers. Fruit bats perform an extremely important function as seed dispersers; many plants depend on bats to scatter their seeds. Nectar eating bats, like bees and many other insects, are important pollinators. Many plant species depend almost entirely on bats for pollination.

A few bats eat fish, which they capture by flying low over the water's surface and gaffing the fish with their exceptionally long claws. A few species eat the flesh of other animals, including mice, birds, frogs, and even other bats. Vampire bats feed exclusively on blood.

Four U.S. bats—the lesser long-nosed bat (pictured here), greater long-nosed bat, Mexican long-tongued bat, and Jamaican fruit-eating bat—include nectar in their diets.

White-winged vampire bats (Diaemus youngi) feed on blood from a chicken.

Vampire Bats

Most famous (or infamous) among bats are the three species of vampire bats of Mexico, Central America, and South America, which feed on the blood of warm-blooded animals. Vampire bats obtain blood by biting their victims with their very sharp incisor teeth and then lapping (not sucking) blood as it flows from the wound. The common vampire bat weighs only about 35 grams (1.23 ounces) and has a wingspan of approximately 50 centimeters (20 inches), although in horror movies they often are depicted as being much larger. There is only one record of a vampire bat in the United States. A hairy-legged vampire bat *(Diphylla ecaudata)* was found in a Texas railroad tunnel several years ago. This bat was over 700 kilometers (435 miles) north of its usual known range in Mexico. The more common vampire bat *(Desmodus rotundus)*, the species that feeds on blood of any terrestrial vertebrate (the other two species feed mainly on blood of birds), has been recorded in Mexico within 200 kilometers (125 miles) of the United States.

Scientists collect guano samples in Blowing Wind Cave, Alabama

Bat Guano

It is well known that bat droppings or "guano" make excellent fertilizer. Certain caves are mined for this valuable material, and some reportedly once contained thousands of tons of guano until much of it was removed for use as fertilizer. Over 100,000 tons (91 million kilograms) of guano was mined from Carlsbad Cavern in New Mexico in the early 1900s. Several "peter" caves were involved in Civil War history. The Confederate army, for example, mined nitrogen-rich earth and guano from several southeastern United States bat caves to produce saltpeter (potassium nitrate) for use in manufacturing gunpowder. At one such operation, at an Arkansas cave now on Buffalo National River lands, the Confederate Army in 1862 constructed 14 buildings and several pieces of machinery. The Confederate saltpeter operation continued until January 10, 1863, when it was captured and destroyed by Union soldiers of the Iowa Cavalry.

Bats as Food

In some parts of the world, especially in parts of Asia, Africa, and the Pacific Islands, many bat species are used as food by humans. On Guam, for example, people sometimes pay exorbitant prices for a bat dinner. One recipe calls for cooking a fruit bat in a mixture of coconut milk, water, spices, and onions. It is then eaten whole, including fur, wings, and internal organs. There is concern that many food species may become extinct due to overharvest and lack of adequate management. This is true, not only for the larger "meatier" species, but for many smaller bats as well.

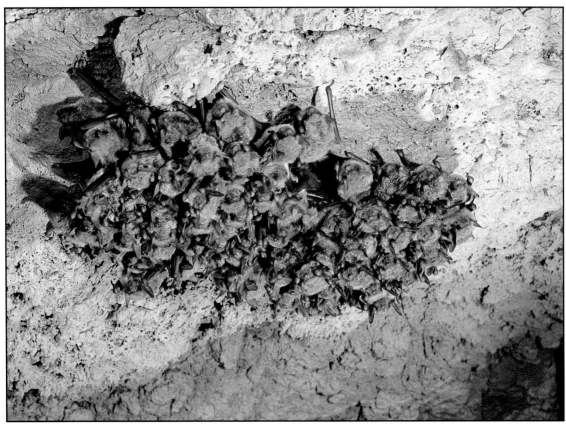

*A **hibernating cluster of cave bats*** (Myotis velifer).

Hibernation and Migration

Most United States cave bats spend winter hibernating in caves (or mines) and move to trees or buildings during summer. A few species reside in caves year-round, although different caves usually are used in summer and winter.

Tree bats seldom enter caves. They roost in trees during summer days and spend winter primarily in hollow trees. Several species make relatively long migration flights between winter and summer habitats. The millions of Brazilian (or Mexican) free-tailed bats that spend the summer in southwestern United States caves, such as Carlsbad Cavern in New Mexico, migrate up to 1,300 kilometers (800 miles) to and from their winter roosts in Mexico. Most cave bats are very loyal to certain caves and return year after year to the same caves, often to the exact location in the cave where they spent the previous winter.

Because insects are not available as food during winter, temperate-zone bats survive by either migrating to warmer regions where insects are available, or by hibernating. Hibernation is a state of torpor during which normal metabolic activities are greatly reduced. Body temperature in hibernating bats is reduced from over 100° F (42° C) to that of the hibernation site, usually 40-60° F (4-15° C). The heart rate is slowed from over 1,000 beats per minute (bat in flight) to only one beat every four or five seconds. A hibernating bat can thus survive on only a few grams of stored fat during the approximately five-to-six month hibernation period. Bats usually lose from one-fourth to one-half their pre-hibernation weight during hibernation.

Several bat species hibernate in dense clusters on cave walls or ceilings. Clusters may consist of hundreds of bats per square foot, depending on the size of the species involved. Summer "maternity" colonies of pregnant or nursing females of several species also congregate and cluster together. The combined body heat of bats in maternity colonies that rear their young in caves serves to raise the temperature of the colony site to a higher and more optimum temperature for development of the young.

Little brown bat (Myotis lucifugus)

Homing Instinct

Many bat species exhibit homing instinct, the ability to return home after being displaced into unfamiliar territory. In an experiment several years ago, bats were removed from their Kentucky hibernation cave in October shortly after arriving from their summer habitat. Three groups of 500 bats each were transported to sites 322 kilometers (200 miles) from the cave, banded, and released. Within only a few weeks, over 67 percent found their way back from one of their release sites. Many others quite likely returned undetected, because there were numerous inaccessible cracks and crevices in the cave where bats could hide. How bats home over such great distances remains a mystery.

Reproduction and Longevity

Most female bats produce only one offspring per year, although some species give birth to three or four babies at a time. Most United States bats breed in autumn, and the females store sperm until the following spring when fertilization takes place. The gestation period lasts only a few weeks, and baby bats are born in May or June. They develop rapidly, and most can learn to fly within two to five weeks after birth. Bats live relatively long lives for animals of their small size, some as long as 30 years, as evidenced from bat banding studies.

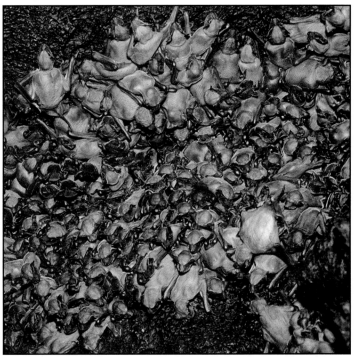

Juvenile Brazilian free-tailed bats (Tadarida brasiliensis).

Bat "Bombs"

One of the most interesting bat stories concerns the planned use of bats to carry weapons during World War II. The plan was called "Project X-Ray" and was to be carried out by the U. S. Navy. It entailed using thousands of Brazilian free-tailed bats, the species inhabiting such caves as Carlsbad Cavern in New Mexico and often inhabiting buildings in the southeastern United States. Each bat was to carry a one-ounce napalm incendiary bomb equipped with a chemical timer. Each bomb would produce a 55 centimeter (22-inch) flame and would burn for seven to 10 minutes. It was intended that the bomb-carrying bats would be dropped in cages by parachute (approximately 7,000 per cage and parachute) over certain Japanese cities. Automatic devices would open the cages and release the bats before reaching the ground. The bats would then disperse into buildings, hopefully free themselves from the incendiary bombs, and the bombs would start numerous fires resulting in widespread destruction.

Although planning and testing were carried out over a two-year period, the plan ultimately was abandoned, probably because of the development of the atomic bomb. The scheme would probably have been very effective, as evidenced by the fact that during one of the "bat war games" tests, one of the buildings at the military base where they were being conducted was destroyed by a "bat bomb."

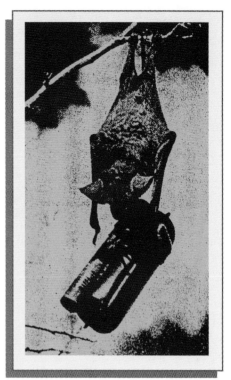

Bat carrying incendiary bomb.

The steel gate closing this mine portal allows free access to bats while preventing human entry.

Mines and Bridges

Abandoned mines and highway bridges are important habitats for many species of bats. Bats often occupy abandoned mines where they raise their young during summer and hibernate in winter. Many of the largest remaining United States bat populations roost in mines. Joints between structural components of bridges and other man-made structures often serve as sites for maternity, hibernation, and day roosts. The Congress Avenue bridge, over the Colorado River in downtown Austin, Texas, serves as a maternity roost for a colony of Brazilian free-tailed bats numbering 600,000 individuals.

Thanks to cooperative efforts between conservation organizations, private companies, and government agencies, mines that would have been permanently sealed are being closed with bat-friendly gates to allow bats to inhabit the mines and to prevent humans from entering these potentially dangerous sites. An abandoned iron mine in Wisconsin, for example, now houses a winter hibernating population of over 100,000 bats. In addition to allowing access to mines by bats, significant efforts are being made to add bat-friendly features to bridges and other man-made structures.

Controlling "Nuisance" Bats

The news media are often guilty of sensationalizing stories about rabid bats or bat colonies in buildings and the dangers involved. Even some nationally known and respected magazines have published ridiculous bat scare stories. One such article, "The Nightmare House," described the experiences of a family that didn't know "there was another presence in the house, strange and ominous, that was soon to shatter the quiet and suddenly plunge them into terror." A few unscrupulous pest control companies have charged exorbitant fees for removing (killing) bat colonies from the homes of "terrified" people.

A few species of United States bats, given the opportunity, may take up residence in attics or other parts of buildings, and most people prefer not to have "bats in their belfries" or anywhere in their residences. In many cases, the best method of preventing bats from roosting in houses or other buildings is simply closing the openings through which they enter. This should be done during the time of year when bats are not present (usually September through March) or at night after bats leave to forage. Care also should be taken not to trap flightless young in buildings.

Chemical toxicants never should be used to solve bat problems in buildings. They usually are unnecessary and may create far worse problems, because these poisons may be dangerous to humans or their use may cause poisoned bats to fall to the ground where they die slowly and are more likely to come into contact with children or pets. A 1982 U.S. Fish and Wildlife Service publication (Resource Publication 143) entitled "House Bat Management," by Arthur M. Greenhall, is available from the Superintendent of Documents, U.S. Government Printing Office, Washington, DC 20402. It is highly recommended as an aid in solving house-bat problems. Batproofing procedures often also result in energy conservation.

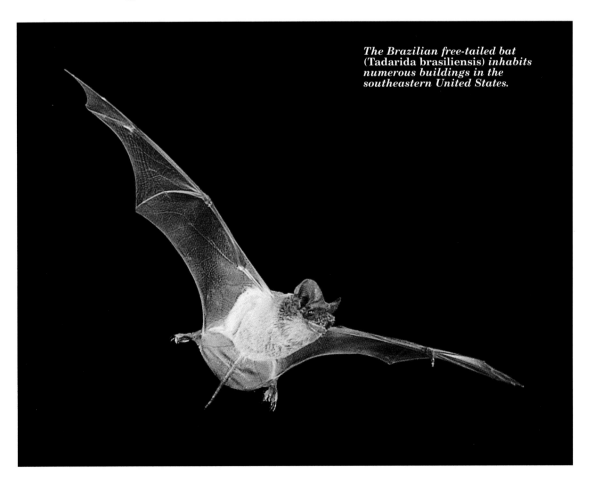

The Brazilian free-tailed bat (Tadarida brasiliensis) *inhabits numerous buildings in the southeastern United States.*

Attracting Bats

An attempt once was made in San Antonio, Texas, to attract bats to wooden "municipal bat roosts." It was hoped the bats would eradicate mosquitoes and thus malaria, as well as supply guano for fertilizer. But, relatively few bats used the structures. Similar structures have been built more recently elsewhere and many have successfully attracted bats. A large bat house on the campus of the University of Florida in Gainesville houses a colony of Brazilian free-tailed bats estimated to number 50,000. As people discover bats are beneficial and not dangerous, more and more attempt to attract bats, in much the way they attract certain songbirds. Many Europeans and more recently Americans, have placed bat houses in their yards to take advantage of bats' insect-eating habits. "Suggestions for Building Bat Houses and Attracting Bats" is available from Bat Conservation International, Inc., P. O. Box 162603, Austin, Texas 78716-2603. This organization also markets preconstructed bat houses as well as other bat-related items such as literature, posters, and jewelry.

Small "rocket box" style bat house.

Large bat houses have been built to attract bats.

Rabies

Bats, like many other mammals, can contract and transmit rabies as well as other diseases. Although rabies has been found at one time or another in many species of bats in the United States, it is relatively uncommon. Rabid bats seldom are aggressive. Fewer than 40 people in the United States are known to have contracted rabies from bats during the past 40 years; in fact, rabies was not known to occur in bats until the 1950s. Far more people are killed by dog attacks (10-20 annually), bee stings, power mowers, or lightning than rabies from bats. However, because bats can carry and transmit rabies, they should not be handled. This is especially true for bats found on the ground, because these may be unhealthy.

Threats to Bats

Several animals, including owls, hawks, raccoons, skunks, and snakes prey on bats; yet, relatively few animals consume bats as a regular part of their diet. Man seems to be the only animal having significant impact on bat populations. Adverse human impacts include habitat destruction, direct killing, vandalism, disturbance of hibernating and maternity colonies, use of pesticides (on their food—insects), and other chemical toxicants. Drastic reductions in bat populations have occurred during recent years in the United States and worldwide.

A Trans-Pecos rat snake feeds on a Brazilian free-tailed bat (Tadarida brasiliensis).

Human disturbance to hibernation and maternity colonies is a major factor in the decline of many bat species. Even well meaning individuals such as spelunkers (cave explorers) and biologists cause these disturbances. Hibernating bats arouse from hibernation when disturbed by people entering their caves. When aroused, they use up precious winter fat needed to support them until insects are again available in spring. A single arousal probably costs a bat as much energy as it would normally expend in two to three weeks of hibernation. Thus, if aroused often, hibernating bats may starve to death before spring.

Disturbance to summer maternity colonies also is extremely detrimental. Maternity colonies won't tolerate disturbance, especially when flightless newborn young are present. Baby bats may be dropped to their deaths or abandoned by panicked parents if disturbance occurs during this period.

How You Can Help

People can help preserve our beneficial bats by following these common-sense guidelines:

✔ Avoid maternity colonies and hibernating bats. Even slight disturbance is harmful to bats.

✔ Cave habitats are fragile and easily disturbed. If you must enter caves, do so only as an observer. Leave everything as you found it. And remember, disturbing or harming endangered bats is a federal offense carrying serious penalties.

✔ Never shoot, poison, or otherwise harm bats. Bats are extremely beneficial insect eaters, and nuisance bats can be encouraged to move elsewhere.

Status of United States Bats

Of the 45 United States bats species, six are wholly or partially (i.e., certain subspecies) considered endangered (in danger of extinction throughout all or a significant portion of their range) by the U. S. Fish and Wildlife Service as well as most state wildlife agencies. Twenty additional species or subspecies are considered to be of special concern and may be proposed for listing as threatened or endangered in the future. Populations of several of the remaining species, especially cave-dwelling species, also appear to be declining.

Because of concern for the welfare of endangered, as well as other cave bat species, the necessity for protection and management of these species and their most critical habitat became evident. Before management recommendations were formulated, studies were conducted to obtain pertinent data concerning distribution, status, and ecology of these species.

Fine nylon mist nets capture bats needed for study—in this case, a big brown bat (Eptesicus fuscus).

Studies were initiated by several federal and state agencies. Primary objectives were to determine distribution and status of endangered and special-concern species, to obtain information concerning various aspects of their ecology, and to formulate management recommendations. Gathering data about other non-endangered bat species was an additional objective.

Techniques used included searching caves previously known to be inhabited by bats and attempting to locate additional bat caves. In addition to identifying important bat caves, sampling for the presence of bats was done by mist-netting or by using bat traps at numerous locations.

Mist nets are large (up to 3 x 18 meters) (10 x 60 feet) nets made of very fine thread that are used to capture flying bats. Bat traps consist of two frames a few inches apart over which are strung very thin vertical wires, one inch (2.5 centimeters) apart. Bats flying into a trap detect and avoid the first set of wires, then hit the second set of wires and fall unharmed into a collecting bag.

Observations of bat activity were made using night-vision (starlight) scopes and with ultrasonic bat detectors, devices that render ultrasonic bat cries audible to human ears. On some occasions, bats were fitted with small vials containing a chemical light substance (Cyalume) to study flight behavior and determine foraging habitat and movements. Some bats also were studied by fitting them with tiny radio transmitters and tracking their movements with directional antennae and radio receivers.

Bat researcher removes bat from mist net.

Bats, like birds, can be banded for later recognition. A numbered band is placed on the bat's forearm.

To study migration and movement patterns, numerous bats were banded with colored, celluloid, numbered, wing bands or with numbered metal bands provided by the U.S. Fish and Wildlife Service. Temperature and humidity at roost sites also were obtained. Other data gathered included information on sex ratios, reproduction, swarming, longevity, food habits, mortality, effects of cave gates and fences, and various other behavioral and ecological data. Long-term monitoring programs were initiated to determine population trends over time and to ascertain the effectiveness of management measures already initiated.

The U.S. Fish and Wildlife Service has had Recovery Plans prepared for endangered bats by Recovery Teams comprised of experts. Many protective management measures already have been taken, as recommended in the Recovery Plans. These include gating or fencing important caves and placing warning/interpretive signs at other caves to minimize human disturbance to bat colonies. Signs placed at selected cave entrances tell what endangered bat species inhabit the cave, the season when they are present, information concerning bats' beneficial nature, and adverse effects of disturbing bat colonies. Signs also point out that entering these caves during restricted times is a violation of the Federal Endangered Species Act, punishable by fines of up $50,000 for each violation.

Several state and federal agencies and organizations are now actively involved in bat conservation. These include state wildlife agencies, U.S. Fish and Wildlife Service, U.S. Forest Service, National Park Service, Bureau of Land Management, U.S. Army Corps of Engineers, Tennessee Valley Authority, Biological Resources Division of the U.S. Geological Survey, state parks, natural heritage commissions, Nature Conservancy, National Speleological Society, Cave Research Foundation, American Cave Conservation Association, and Bat Conservation International. Members of several other organizations and numerous private landowners and other individuals also are involved. All should be commended for their efforts.

Information concerning the location of additional important bat caves is needed as part of the continuing conservation effort. Individuals with knowledge of caves containing bat colonies should contact appropriate wildlife-agency personnel.

A night-vision scope provides a means of observing bats in almost total darkness.

Bats of the United States

Family Mormoopidae
Mormoops megalophylla........ Ghost-faced Bat

Family Phyllostomidae
Macrotus californicus........... California Leaf-nosed Bat (Of Special Concern)
Choeronycteris mexicana....... Mexican Long-tongued Bat (Of Special Concern)
Leptonycteris curasoae.......... Lesser Long-nosed Bat
    L. c. yerbabuenae.............. Lesser Long-nosed Bat (Endangered)
Leptonycteris nivalis............. Greater Long-nosed Bat (Endangered)
Artibeus jamaicensis............. Jamaican Fruit-eating Bat

Family Vespertilionidae
Antrozous pallidus................. Pallid Bat
Eptesicus fuscus..................... Big Brown Bat
Euderma maculatum............. Spotted Bat (Of Special Concern)
Idionycteris phyllotis............. Allen's Big-eared Bat (Of Special Concern)
Lasionycteris noctivagans...... Silver-haired Bat
Lasiurus blossevillii............... Western Red Bat
Lasiurus borealis................... Eastern Red Bat
Lasiurus cinereus.................. Hoary Bat
    L. c. semotus...................... Hawaiian Hoary Bat (Endangered)
Lasiurus ega........................... Southern Yellow Bat
Lasiurus intermedius............. Northern Yellow Bat
Lasiurus seminolus................ Seminole Bat
Lasiurus xanthinus................ Western Yellow Bat
Myotis auriculus.................... Southwestern Bat
Myotis austroriparius............ Southeastern Bat (Of Special Concern)
Myotis californicus................ California Bat
Myotis ciliolabrum................ Western Small-footed Bat (Of Special Concern)
Myotis evotis.......................... Western Long-eared Bat (Of Special Concern)
Myotis grisescens................... Gray Bat (Endangered)

Outflight of Brazilian free-tailed bats **(Tadarida brasiliensis)** *from Lava Cave in New Mexico.*

16

Myotis keenii........................	Keen's Bat
Myotis leibii.........................	Eastern Small-footed Bat (Of Special Concern)
Myotis lucifugus...................	Little Brown Bat
M. l. occultus...................	Arizona Bat (Of Special Concern)
Myotis septentrionalis..........	Northern Long-eared Bat
Myotis sodalis.......................	Indiana Bat (Endangered)
Myotis thysanodes................	Fringed Bat (Of Special Concern)
Myotis velifer........................	Cave Bat (Of Special Concern)
Myotis volans........................	Long-legged Bat (Of Special Concern)
Myotis yumanensis................	Yuma Bat (Of Special Concern)
Nycticeius humeralis............	Evening Bat
Pipistrellus hesperus............	Western Pipistrelle Bat
Pipistrellus subflavus...........	Eastern Pipistrelle Bat
Corynorhinus rafinesquii.....	Rafinesque's Big-eared Bat (Of Special Concern)
Corynorhinus townsendii.....	Townsend's Big-eared Bat
C. t. virginianus...............	Virginia Big-eared Bat (Endangered)
C. t. ingens......................	Ozark Big-eared Bat (Endangered)
C. t. pallescens.................	Western Big-eared Bat (Of Special Concern)
C. t. townsendii...............	Townsend's Big-eared Bat (Of Special Concern)

Family Molossidae

Eumops glaucinus................	Wagner's Mastiff Bat
E. g. floridanus...............	Florida Mastiff Bat (Of Special Concern)
Eumops perotis.....................	Greater Mastiff Bat
E. p. californicus.............	Western Mastiff Bat (Of Special Concern)
Eumops underwoodi.............	Underwood's Mastiff Bat (Of Special Concern)
Molossus molossus................	Pallas' Mastiff Bat
Nyctinomops femorosaccus...	Pocketed Free-tailed Bat
Nyctinomops macrotis..........	Big Free-tailed Bat (Of Special Concern)
Tadarida brasiliensis...........	Brazilian Free-tailed Bat

Allen's big-eared bat (**Idionycteris phyllotis**) *is one of several U.S. bat species or subspecies whose status is of special concern.*

Species Accounts

Ghost-faced Bat

Mormoops megalophylla

Weight is 13-19 grams (0.5-0.6 ounce), wingspan is 35-40 centimeters (14-16 inches), and distribution is southern Arizona, New Mexico, and Texas, throughout most of Mexico (except northwestern region), then southward into Central America. Ghost-faced bats usually occur in lowland areas, especially desert scrub and riverine habitats, where they often roost in caves, tunnels, and mine shafts, but they also have been found in old buildings. Although they may congregate in large numbers at a roosting site, this species tends not to form compact clusters. Instead, members of the colony roost singly, spread about 15 centimeters (6 inches) apart over the ceiling of a cave. When asleep, individuals rest with the back arched and the head tucked almost to the chest. The ghost-faced bat emerges late in the evening, and its flight is strong and swift. In Mexico, this species produces large deposits of guano (feces). This material, rich in nitrogen from the exoskeletons of the insects upon which the bats feed, is used by local people as fertilizer. Foods include large moths and other insects. One baby is born in late May or early June. Ghost-faced bats are common winter residents in caves along the southern edge of the Edwards Plateau, Texas, but its occurrence at specific localities is highly variable and unpredictable.

California Leaf-nosed Bat *Macrotus californicus*

Weight is 8-17 grams (0.3-0.6 ounce), wingspan is 33-38 centimeters (13-15 inches), and distribution is the southwestern United States, western and southern Mexico, and northern Central America. This rather large bat resides in lowland desert habitat. Abandoned mine tunnels are its favored daytime retreat because they provide protection from the heat and drying effects of the desert climate. When at rest, it hangs pendant by gripping the ceiling of its roost with one or both feet. Much of the time at rest is spent hanging from a single foot with the other leg relaxed and dangling to the side. The free foot often is used for scratching and grooming as the bat swings gently, like a pendulum. Like most other bats, this species uses resting places during its nocturnal forays. These night roosts may be open buildings, cellars, porches, bridges, rock shelters, and mines. Emergence from the day roost begins about an hour after sunset, considerably later than for most other species of bats, and is spread over about three hours, with small groups of bats often leaving together. Grasshoppers, cicadas, moths, caterpillars, and beetles are consumed. Remains of sphinx moths, butterflies, and dragonflies have been found beneath night roosts. Although twins are known, usually one baby is born sometime between mid-May and mid-July. This species is of special concern.

19

Mexican Long-tongued Bat — *Choeronycteris mexicana*

Weight is 10-25 grams (0.4-0.9 ounce), wingspan is 33-38 centimeters (13-15 inches), and distribution includes the southwestern United States, most of Mexico, and Central America. This is a rather large bat with a long, slender nose. It occupies a variety of vegetative habitats ranging from arid thorn shrub to tropical deciduous forest and mixed oak-conifer forest. It is believed to migrate seasonally to take advantage of suitable sources of food. Buildings and culverts occasionally are occupied, but caves and abandoned mines seem to be favored as daytime roosts; these bats hang in dimly lit areas near the entrances, so even small caves are occupied. In roosts, they do not cluster, but hang 2-5 centimeters (1-2 inches) apart, usually by only one foot, so that they can rotate 360° to detect predators. They are extremely wary, thus easily disturbed, and readily leave the roost. They seem to prefer flying out into open daylight rather than retreating deeper into large shelters. In flight, the wings make a swishing sound similar to that produced by long-nosed bats. Foods include fruits, pollen, nectar, and insects. One baby is born in June or July, but parturition may be as late as September in Mexico. As with many other bats, the fetus is about 30% of mother's weight. Parturition takes about 15 minutes. Babies are born in a remarkably advanced state of development and are surprisingly well furred. A mother may carry her rather large baby while foraging. This species is rare in the United States and is considered to be of special concern.

Lesser Long-nosed Bat — *Leptonycteris curasoae*

Weight is 21-23 grams (0.7-0.8 ounce), wingspan is 36-40 centimeters (14-16 inches), and distribution is from the southwestern United States to southern Mexico. A resident of desert-scrub country, the lesser long-nosed bat is colonial, occupying mines and caves at the base of mountains where the alluvial fan supports agaves, yuccas, saguaros, and organ pipe cacti. It hangs with its feet so close together it can turn nearly 360° to watch for predators. Like other leaf-nosed bats, it takes flight when disturbed. When launching, it gives several strong wing beats, bringing the body into a horizontal position before releasing its grip. It is an agile flier and can fly nearly straight up while maintaining a horizontal body position. Flight is rapid and direct, but the bats can hover momentarily and maneuver well. It emerges within about one hour after sundown. The long tongue, covered with hair-like papillae toward the tip, is well adapted for feeding at flowers. These bats may land on the flowering stalk of agaves and insert their long snouts into each blossom. After feeding, the stomach is so distended the bat appears to be in late pregnancy. When the stomach is filled, they retire to a night roost where they hang and rest. Nectar, pollen, and insects are consumed, but fruits are eaten after the flowering season is past. One baby is born in late May or June. Maternity colonies may harbor thousands of individuals. The subspecies occurring in the United States, *L. c. yerbabuenae*, is considered endangered.

Greater Long-nosed Bat *Leptonycteris nivalis*

Weight is 23-25 grams (0.8-0.9 ounce), wingspan is 40-44 centimeters (16-17 inches), and the distribution extends from the Big Bend region of Texas, southward across most of Mexico to central Guatemala. This is a colonial cave dweller that usually inhabits deep caverns, but also found in mines, culverts, hollow trees, and unoccupied buildings. This bat occupies a variety of habitats from high-elevation, pine-oak woodlands to sparsely vegetated deserts. The muzzle is greatly lengthened, and this bat has a long protrusive tongue attached to the posterior sternum. There are rows of hairlike projections covering the area near the tip of the tongue, which aid in acquiring nectar. It emerges relatively late in the evening to feed. It is an agile flyer, capable of quick maneuvering and relatively high-speed flight. It makes swooshing sounds as it flies and can fly straight up while maintaining a horizontal body position. It primarily feeds on nectar, pollen, insects, and soft, succulent fruits of cactus during the non-flowering season. When foraging at agaves, it crawls down the stalk, thrusts its snout into the flowers, and licks nectar with its long tongue, which can be extended up to 7.5 centimeters (3 inches) and can reach nectar at the base of the flowers. It emerges from the flowers covered with pollen and is an effective pollinator of many cacti, agaves, and other plants. One baby is born in April, May, or June. It is rare in the United States and is considered endangered.

Jamaican Fruit-eating Bat   *Artibeus jamaicensis*

Weight is 42-44 grams (1.5-1.6 ounces), wingspan is 44-48 centimeters (17-19 inches), and this fruit bat is widely distributed from northern Sinaloa, Mexico, and from the Florida Keys southward through the Caribbean and northern South America. The Jamaican fruit-eating bat forages in small groups. Captured individuals may produce stress calls, which induce "mobbing" behavior by other members of the group. These bats are less active on bright moonlit nights than on dark nights. Roosts may be in buildings, caves, or hollow trees. Sometimes they build tents by biting the midribs, causing them to fold. Possible predators include owls and falcons. The species eats mostly fruits of fig trees but also mangos, avocados, and bananas. It also feeds on pollen, nectar, flower parts, and sometimes insects. Food passes through the digestive tract in 15-20 minutes. The reproductive period of the Jamaican fruit-eating bat is closely tied to the maximum abundance of figs. The species is polygynous; males may accumulate harems of up to 25 females. Besides harems, Jamaican fruit-eating bats also form groups of bachelor males and groups of non-reproductive females. Usually, one baby is born to each female in March and April, but twins also may be born. Lifespan may be 7-10 years. Rare in the United States, this species is known only from the Florida Keys. Elsewhere in its range, the Jamaican fruit-eating bat often is one of the most common bats.

Pallid Bat

Antrozous pallidus

Weight is 20-35 grams (0.7-1.2 ounces), wingspan is 37-41 centimeters (15-16 inches), and distribution is southcentral British Columbia to central Mexico. The pallid bat is common in arid regions with rocky outcroppings, particularly near water. This gregarious species usually roosts in small colonies of 20 or more individuals in rock crevices and buildings, but occasionally roosts in caves, mines, rock piles, and tree cavities. Relative to other bats, pallid bats emerge from roosts relatively late, but the time of evening emergence varies seasonally. Mothers and offspring may emerge and forage together. Pallid bats walk on the ground with a variety of strides and gaits, and they can hover or glide momentarily. They chiefly feed on large (2-7 centimeters or 1-3 inches, in length) prey that is taken on the ground or, perhaps less frequently, in flight within a few meters of the ground or from the surfaces of vegetation. Prey items include flightless arthropods such as scorpions, crickets, and centipedes (see inside cover), ground-roving insects such as darkling ground beetles, scarab beetles, predacious ground beetles, carrion beetles, and short-horned grasshoppers, and prey that are gleaned from vegetation, including cicadas, katydids, praying mantids, long-horned beetles, and sphingid moths. Pallid bats also are known to eat lizards and rodents. One or two babies are born in May or June. Females hang upright during parturition, and newborns are held in the curled interfemoral membrane. This is a common species throughout most of its range.

24

Big Brown Bat   *Eptesicus fuscus*

Weight is 14-21 grams (0.5-0.7 ounce), wingspan is 32-40 centimeters (13-16 inches), and distribution is from southern Canada through southern North America into South America, including many islands in the Caribbean. These bats are closely associated with humans and are familiar to more people in the United States than any other species of bat. Most summer roosts are in attics, barns, bridges, or other man-made structures, where colonies of a few to several hundred individuals gather to form maternity colonies. They move into caves, mines, and other underground structures to hibernate only during the coldest weather. Where most of these bats winter remains unknown. It emerges at dusk and flies a steady, nearly straight course at a height of 6-10 meters (20-33 feet) in route to foraging areas. Its large size and steady flight make it readily recognizable. Apparently, some individuals use the same feeding ground each night, for a bat can sometimes be seen following an identical feeding pattern on different nights. After feeding, the bat flies to a night roost to rest; favored night roosts include garages, breezeways, and porches of houses. These bats consume beetles, ants, flies, mosquitos, mayflies, stoneflies, and other insects. Mating occurs in autumn and winter, females store sperm, and fertilization takes place in spring. In the eastern United States, big brown bats usually bear twins in early June. In the western United States, usually only one baby is born each year. It is common throughout most of its range.

Spotted Bat

Euderma maculatum

Weight is 16-20 grams (0.6-0.7 ounce), wingspan is 34-38 centimeters (13-15 inches), and distribution is from southcentral British Columbia to southern Mexico. This spectacularly colored bat is white underneath and has black fur on its back with three large white spots. The spotted bat occurs in a wide range of habitats in the western regions of the continent, most often in rough, rocky, semi-arid, and arid terrain, varying from ponderosa pine forest to scrub country and open desert. The day roosts often are situated on high cliffs. These bats crawl with ease on both horizontal and vertical surfaces, which facilitates their movement in rock crevices where they roost. Spotted bats emerge about an hour after dark and return to the day roost about an hour before sunrise. They fly high, usually 10-15 meters (33-50 feet), at or above treetop height, and have a loud high-pitched echolocation call that is clearly audible to the human observer at distances of 250 meters (825 feet) or more. Spotted bats sometimes use a foraging strategy that involves hunting a regular circuit and searching clearings in pine forests for prey. These bats display a remarkable punctuality in making their rounds, arriving at various points along their route at the same time every night. In spring, they spend 3-5 minutes per clearing, but more time is spent around the same area in summer. Diet consists primarily of moths. One baby is born in June. When born, babies lack the color pattern of adults and weigh about 4 grams. It is one of the rarest bats in North America and is of special concern.

26

Allen's Big-eared Bat   *Idionycteris phyllotis*

Weight is 8-16 grams (0.3-0.6 ounce), wingspan is 31-35 centimeters (12-14 inches), and distribution is the southwestern United States to central Mexico. This is a rather large bat with enormous ears and a unique pair of lappets projecting from the median bases of the ears over the top of the snout. When at rest, the huge ears lie along the back, often curled into the shape of ram's horns. Allen's big-eared bat usually inhabits forested areas of the mountainous Southwest, and is relatively common in pine-oak forested canyons and coniferous forests, but it also may occur in non-forested, arid habitats. At most sites where this species occurs, cliffs, outcroppings, boulder piles, or lava flows are nearby. Day roosts may include rock shelters, caves, and mines. It leaves the roost only after complete darkness, and usually flies about 10 meters (33 feet) above ground. It emits loud calls at about 1-second intervals. Flight is slower than the free-tailed bats, but swifter than most other bats. In close quarters, this species flies slowly, is highly maneuverable, able to hover, and can fly vertically. In more open situations, it uses fast, direct flight. The sexes segregate geographically during summer months, with females gathering into maternity colonies and males possibly remaining solitary, roosting elsewhere. Seasonal movements and winter whereabouts and activities are unknown. Primarily small moths, but soldier beetles, dung beetles, leaf beetles, roaches, and flying ants also are eaten. One baby is born in June or July. Locally common, but rare over most of its range, it is a species of special concern.

Silver-haired Bat

Lasionycteris noctivagans

Weight is 8-11 grams (0.3-0.4 ounce), wingspan is 27-32 centimeters (11-13 inches), and distribution is southern Alaska across southern Canada and southward through much of the United States to northeastern Mexico. A typical day roost is under loose tree bark, but these bats have been found in woodpecker holes and bird nests. Although they may appear in any kind of building, they favor open sheds, garages, and outbuildings rather than enclosed attics. During migration, they may be encountered in a variety of other shelters including piles of slabs, railroad ties, lumber, and fenceposts. Silver-haired bats are rather common locally in migration during about a 2-week period in May in Illinois and in April in Kentucky and Tennessee. Autumn migration is spread over a longer period and these bats seem less common. They hibernate in trees, buildings, rock crevices, and similar protected shelters. This species emerges earlier than most and is easily recognized in flight; it is one of the slowest flying bats in North America. It forages over woodland ponds and streams at heights up to 7 meters (23 feet) and sometimes flies repeatedly over the same circuit during the evening. Silver-haired bats consume insects including moths, true bugs, flies, mosquitos, termites, and beetles. Young apparently are raised in the northern tier of states and northward into Canada. Most females apparently give birth to twins in June or early July. This bat is relatively uncommon throughout much of its range, especially in the southeastern United States.

Western Red Bat   *Lasiurus blossevillii*

Weight is 10-15 grams (0.4-0.5 ounce), wingspan is 28-32 centimeters (11-13 inches), and distribution is western Canada, western United States, western Mexico, and Central America. This solitary species roosts in the foliage of large shrubs and trees in habitats bordering forests, rivers, cultivated fields, and urban areas. In the southwestern United States, the western red bat occurs in streamside habitats dominated by cottonwoods, oaks, sycamores, and walnuts, and rarely is found in desert habitats. In Mexico, it occurs in streamside, arid thorn scrub and pine-oak forests. This species is believed to be migratory in much of the Southwest and has been reported there only during summer months. There are various accounts of its presence during winter and summer in California. For example, the western red bat is resident through winter (September to May) in the vicinity of San Francisco, but absent in summer, and about 100 kilometers (60 miles) to the northeast it is absent in winter, but appears in February or March. The western red bat consumes a variety of moths and other insects. Few data on reproductive biology are available. In mid-May to late June, up to three babies may be born. It is common throughout its range.

Eastern Red Bat   *Lasiurus borealis*

Weight is 9-15 grams (0.3-0.5 ounce), wingspan is 28-33 centimeters (11-13 inches), and distribution includes southern Canada, the eastern United States (except the Florida Peninsula), and northeastern Mexico. Eastern red bats spend daylight hours hanging in foliage of trees. They usually hang by one foot, giving them the appearance of dead leaves. Although these bats seldom enter caves for any distance, they often swarm about cave entrances in autumn. In colder parts of their range, they may migrate south in winter or hibernate in hollow trees or leaf litter. These bats are almost completely furred, except for the ears and parts of the wings, and they can respond to subfreezing temperatures by increasing their metabolism. Predators include several kinds of birds, especially blue jays. Eastern red bats emerge early in the evening and often fly on warm winter afternoons. They forage regularly over the same territory on successive nights. They commonly feed beneath street lights. Eastern red bats consume moths, crickets, flies, mosquitos, true bugs, beetles, cicadas, and other insects. Eastern red bats mate in flight during August and September, sperm is stored over winter, and females give birth to one to four babies (average is 3.2) during late spring or early summer. Babies are born hairless, with the eyes closed, and they cling to the fur of their mother with their teeth, thumbs, and feet. It is common throughout most of its range.

Hoary Bat   *Lasiurus cinereus*

Weight is 25-30 grams (0.9-1.1 ounces), wingspan is 34-41 centimeters (13-16 inches), and this is the most widespread bat in the Americas, occurring in most of southern Canada and southward through most of South America. It also occurs in Hawaii (where it is the only native land mammal), Iceland, Bermuda, and the Dominican Republic. These are large, heavily furred bats. They spend summer days concealed in the foliage of trees,where they choose a leafy site well-covered above, but open from beneath, generally 3-5 meters (10-17 feet) above the ground and usually at the edge of a clearing. In late summer, they may wander into caves; many of these never find their way out. Because they rarely enter houses, spend the daylight hours well concealed, and generally are rare, they seldom are encountered by humans. Northern populations make long seasonal migrations to and from warmer winter habitats. The sexes apparently are segregated throughout most of the summer range; males are uncommon in the eastern United States at this time. Hoary bats may fly during late afternoon on warm days in winter. Their swift and direct flight pattern and large size make them readily identifiable on the wing in most parts of the range. Moths, true bugs, mosquitos, other insects, and occasionally other bats may be captured as food. Hoary bats bear two babies in mid-May, June, or early July. The young cling to the mother through the day, but are left clinging to a twig or leaf while she forages at night. Although relatively common throughout most of North America, the Hawaiian subspecies, *L. c. semotus* (Hawaiian hoary bat), is considered endangered.

Southern Yellow Bat   *Lasiurus ega*

Weight is 10-15 grams (0.4-0.5 ounce), wingspan is 34-38 centimeters (13-15 inches), and the distribution is from southern Texas through eastern Mexico and Central America into southern South America. Like other members of the genus *Lasiurus*, the southern yellow bat is a tree-roosting species; it often roosts individually on the bark of trees. Palm trees are common roosting sites; most records in the United States are along the Rio Grande near Brownsville, Texas, where it inhabits a natural grove of palm trees. It may be migratory in parts of its range, but it seems to be a year-round resident of the Brownsville area, where it is known to occur in six different months, including December. It does not hibernate, but it does undergo daily torpor. In Venezuela, it usually occurs at elevations below 500 meters (1,650 feet), and is strongly associated with moist habitats and multistratal tropical evergreen forest. Small to medium-sized, night-flying insects are the main food items. Pregnant individuals have been recorded in April and June. One litter of two to four babies (average is 2.9) is born in late-April, May, June, or July. Young are capable of breeding in their first year. It is rare in the United States but common in the southern extreme of its range in Paraguay, Uruguay, and Argentina.

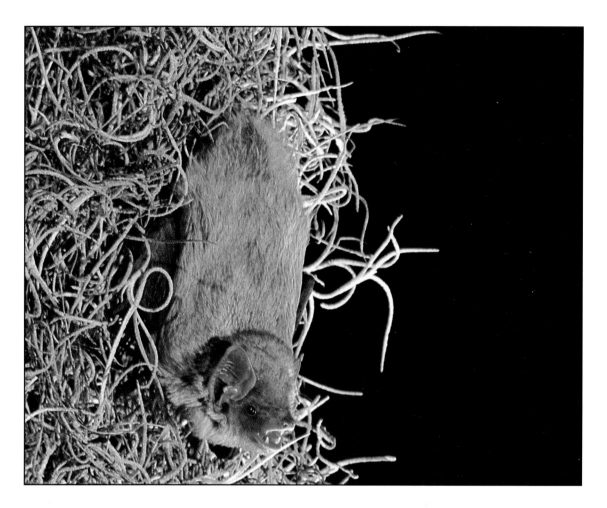

Northern Yellow Bat

Lasiurus intermedius

Weight is 14-31 grams (0.5-1.1 ounces), wingspan is 35-41 centimeters (14-16 inches), and distribution includes the coastal regions of the southeastern United States, eastern Texas, Cuba, and southward into Central America. These bats typically inhabit wooded areas in the vicinity of permanent water. In the southeastern United States, the distribution of northern yellow bats nearly coincides with that of Spanish moss where they often roost and bear their young. A single oak tree, draped with Spanish moss, may harbor several of these bats. In some parts of Florida, it is the most abundant bat. Northern yellow bats are somewhat colonial, especially females during the nursing season. As with other bats, it is doubtful if the mother ever carries her young while foraging, but mothers carry their young when they are flushed from their day roosts. In June-August, when the young have begun to fly, they form evening feeding aggregations with adult females; males rarely are present in these aggregations and are believed to be solitary and scattered at this time of year. Northern yellow bats usually forage 5-7 meters (17-23 feet) above the ground over open areas with few shrubs and only scattered clumps of trees, or along the edge of forests. Grassy areas, such as airports, open pastures, golf courses, and edges of lakes, are favored. True bugs, flies, mosquitos, beetles, and other insects are important components of the diet. Mating occurs in autumn and winter. Two to four babies are born in May or June. Newborn weigh about 3 grams. It is relatively common throughout most of its range.

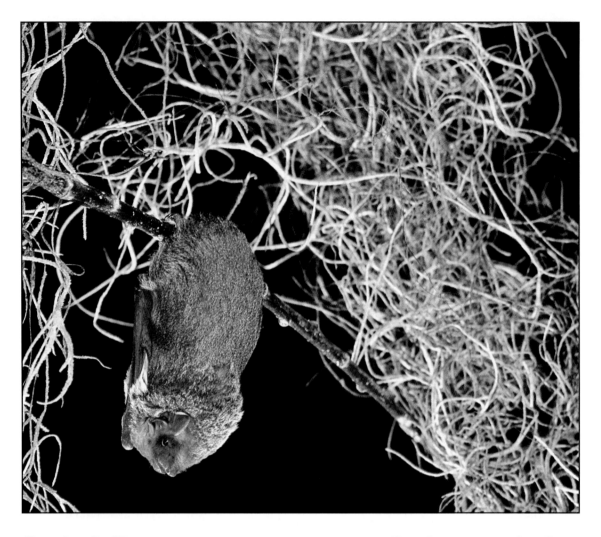

Seminole Bat *Lasiurus seminolus*

Weight is 9-14 grams (0.3-0.5 ounce), wingspan is 29-34 centimeters (11-13 inches), and distribution is the southeastern United States; extralimital records include New York, Pennsylvania, South Texas, Bermuda, and Veracruz, Mexico. The distribution of Seminole bats nearly coincides with that of the Spanish moss where they often roost, but they also are known to roost beneath loose bark, in clumps of foliage, and in caves. These bats often select roost sites in moss hanging on the southwestern exposure of trees. The height above ground of clumps of Spanish moss occupied by Seminole bats is variable, but is great enough for the bat to drop into the unobstructed space beneath when initiating flight. These are the most common bats seen flying in the evening throughout much of the southeastern United States. They fly during all seasons, even on warm evenings in mid-winter. This species emerges early in the evening from daytime roosts and usually feeds at treetop level. The flight is direct and usually rather swift. Seminole bats consume true bugs, flies, mosquitos, beetles, crickets, and other insects, which usually are captured around and in the tree canopy. One to four babies are born during late spring or early summer. Like several other species, Seminole bats apparently wander extensively after the young are weaned, as indicated by late-summer occurrence outside the breeding range. It is common throughout most of its range.

Western Yellow Bat   *Lasiurus xanthinus*

Weight is 10-15 grams (0.4-0.5 ounce), wingspan is 33-37 centimeters (13-15 inches), and distribution is from the southwestern United States across the Mexican Plateau to southern Mexico. Little is known regarding habitat, but like other lasiurine bats, it roosts in leafy vegetation. Ecologically it seems to be associated with the dry thorny vegetation of the Mexican Plateau, coastal western Mexico, including parts of Baja California, and the deserts of the southwestern United States. In New Mexico, it is known to roost in hackberry and sycamore trees. In Arizona, some apparently hibernate among the dead fronds of palm trees, as several were found in these trees in Tucson during January and February. This bat may be extending its range in the United States as evidenced by its appearance at several sites in Arizona in recent years. Recent studies have shown this species is genetically different from the southern yellow bat *(Lasiurus ega)*. It consumes small to medium-sized, night-flying insects. Usually two babies are born in June, but the presence of up to four embryos suggests that size of litter may vary from two to four. It is common in southcentral Arizona but uncommon elsewhere in its range in the United States.

Southwestern Bat   *Myotis auriculus*

Weight is 5-8 grams (0.2-0.3 ounce), wingspan is 26-30 centimeters (10-12 inches), and distribution is from Arizona and New Mexico to southern Mexico, but the winter range is unknown. The southwestern bat often occurs in ponderosa pine forests, but also is present from mesquite and chaparral through the oak forests into the pinyon-juniper habitats, and seems to reach its greatest abundance in areas of extensive rocky cliffs where water is available. No day roosts are known, but night roosts include buildings, mines, and caves. Migrations may result in selection of different habitats during different seasons. This species is most active from 1.5-2.0 hours after sunset, but also may show other peaks of activity during the night. Flight speed is about 13 kilometers per hour (8 miles per hour). Moths are the primary food, and males may eat significantly more moths than females. This bat is known to glean insects, primarily moths with 3-4-centimeter (1-2 inches) wing spans, from buildings and tree trunks; it may land briefly on the substrate, then pick the insect off the surface. One baby usually is born in June or early July, but timing of birth shows considerable geographic variation. Life span is at least 3 years. It is common throughout its range.

Southeastern Bat

Myotis austroriparius

Weight is 5-8 grams (0.2-0.3 ounce), wingspan is 24-29 centimeters (9-11 inches), and distribution includes the southeastern United States from southern Illinois and Indiana to northeastern Texas and northern Florida. Caves are favorite roosting sites, although buildings and other shelters sometimes are used. Maternity colonies comprised of thousands of individuals inhabit caves. Throughout much of the South, these bats reside in buildings and hollow trees, but in the northern part of their range they roost primarily in caves. In winter, they leave the maternity caves and take up residence in small groups at outdoor sites. Predators include opossums, snakes, and owls, but by destruction of roosting sites and killing of these bats, humans are the major threat to the species. Southeastern bats usually are associated with bodies of water, over which they feed.

They forage low, close to the water's surface. A variety of insects are consumed, but the diet of this species has not been studied. Mating time is unknown, but about 90% of pregnant females bear twins in late April or mid-May. The production of twins is unique among bats of the genus *Myotis* in the United States; all other *Myotis* usually produce one baby. Clusters of babies often are separate from adult females during the day. Young bats can fly when 5-6 weeks old. Once common, populations of the southeastern bat have decreased significantly; it is now considered a species of special concern.

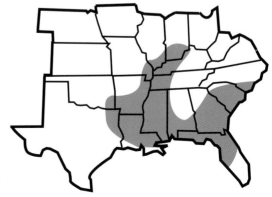

California Bat   *Myotis californicus*

Weight is 3-5 grams (0.1-0.2 ounce), wingspan is 22-26 centimeters (9-10 inches), and distribution is from southern Alaska and western Canada southward through most of Mexico. The California bat is one of the smallest bats in the United States. It occupies a variety of habitats in the Pacific Northwest and southern and western British Columbia, from the humid coastal forest to semidesert, and from sea level to at least 1,800 meters (5,940 feet) elevation. In arid regions, it usually occurs in the vicinity of water. Individuals emerge shortly after sunset to forage, which continues at irregular intervals until dawn. Its flight is slow and erratic and it hunts primarily along margins of tree clumps, around the edge of the tree canopy, over water, and well above ground in open country. California bats roost in rock crevices, hollow trees, spaces under loose bark, and in buildings. The sexes roost separately during summer when females form small maternity colonies, but occur together September to March. They hibernate in caves and mines. The California bat feeds on small flying insects, primarily flies, moths, and beetles. Its foraging strategy consists of locating and feeding in concentrations of insects where its slow maneuverable flight allows it to capture several insects in quick succession over a short distance. Breeding takes place in autumn, and one baby is born in July. Lifespan is about 15 years. It is common throughout its range.

Western Small-footed Bat   *Myotis ciliolabrum*

   Weight is 4-6 grams (0.1-0.2 ounce), wingspan is 21-25 centimeters (8-10 inches), and distribution is from southern British Columbia, Alberta, and Saskatchewan to the southwestern United States. The western small-footed bat seems to prefer arid habitats where it is associated with cliffs, talus fields, and, in the prairies, with clay buttes and steep riverbanks. This species roosts in crevices in rock faces and clay banks, it may use the spaces beneath and between boulders in talus fields, and it also has been found roosting beneath bark and in barns. The western small-footed bat begins its nightly activity at dusk shortly after sunset with peaks of activity between 2200 and 2300 hours and 0100 and 0200 hours. It flies slowly and erratically as it forages as heights of 1-3 meters (3-10 feet) along cliffs and rocky slopes, and it may forage over water when not in association with the California bat, which usually hunts over and near water. In British Columbia, the proportions of different species of prey taken by the western small-footed bat and the California bat are similar. It appears that these species co-exist by spatial partitioning of the available food resource. Hibernation sites include caves and mines. Foods consist of small insects—flies, beetles, and moths. One baby usually is born in June, but twins also occur. This species is of special concern

Western Long-eared Bat   *Myotis evotis*

Weight is 5-8 grams (0.2-0.3 ounce), wingspan is 25-30 centimeters (10-12 inches), and distribution includes southwestern Canada, western United States, and Baja California, Mexico. It occurs in a variety of habitats over its range in North America, but mostly in forested areas. In the Pacific Northwest and British Columbia, it occurs from dry forest to subalpine forest, especially where broken rock outcroppings prevail. Where suitable roosting sites are available, this species also is found in semiarid shrublands, sage, chaparral, and agricultural areas. Females form small maternity colonies in summer, whereas males and non-pregnant females live singly or in small groups, occasionally occupying the same site as a maternity colony, but roosting apart from it. Groups of 12-30 individuals have been found in roosts. Daytime roosts are known to include abandoned buildings, hollow trees, loose slabs of bark, timbers of unused railroad trestles, caves and mines, fissures of cliffs, and sink holes. This species emerges at dusk, and its flight is slow and maneuverable as it forages between and within the treetops and over woodland ponds. Predators include snakes, raccoons, hawks, and owls. Foods include moths, beetles, flies, net-winged insects, and true bugs. Males eat significantly more moths than do females. One baby is born in late June or early July. It has a recorded lifespan of 22 years. This species is of special concern.

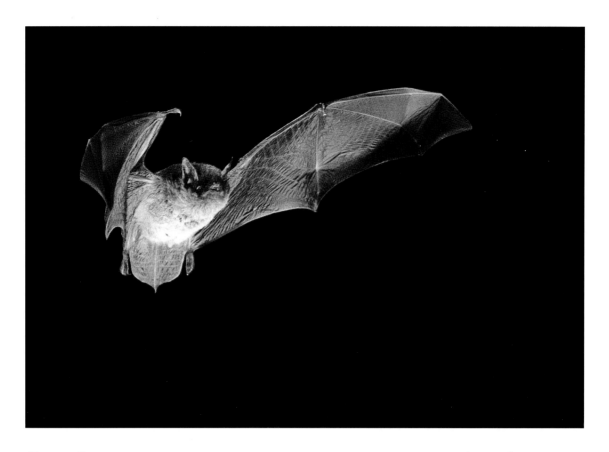

Gray Bat   *Myotis grisescens*

Weight is 8-11 grams (0.3-0.4 ounce), wingspan is 27-32 centimeters (11-13 inches), and distribution includes cave regions of Arkansas, Missouri, Kentucky, Tennessee, and Alabama, with occasional colonies found in adjacent states. Gray bats are cave residents year-round, but different caves usually are occupied in summer and winter. Few have been found roosting outside caves. They hibernate primarily in deep vertical caves with large rooms acting as cold-air traps (5-11°C or 42-52°F). In summer, females form maternity colonies of a few hundred to many thousands of individuals, often in large caves containing streams. Maternity colonies occur in caves that, because of their configuration, trap warm air (14-25°C or 58-77°F) or provide restricted rooms or domed ceilings capable of trapping combined body heat from clustered individuals. Because of their specific habitat requirements, fewer than 5% of available caves are suitable for gray bats. Males and non-reproductive females form bachelor colonies in summer. Gray bats primarily forage over water of rivers and lakes. Moths, beetles, flies, mosquitos, and mayflies are important in the diet, but gray bats also consume a variety of other insects. Mating occurs in September and October, and females enter hibernation immediately after mating, followed by males. Females store sperm through winter and become pregnant after emerging from hibernation. One baby is born in late May or early June, and begins to fly within 20-25 days of birth. Lifespan may exceed 14-15 years. Listed as endangered, about 95% of these bats hibernate in only eight caves, making them extremely vulnerable to destruction.

Keen's Bat   *Myotis keenii*

Weight is 4-6 grams (0.1-0.2 ounce), wingspan is 21-26 centimeters (8-10 inches), and the geographic range of Keen's bat is among the smallest of any bat in North America. The bulk of its range is in British Columbia west of the coastal mountains extending into southeastern Alaska and northwestern Washington. Keen's bat is restricted to the dense coastal forest of the Pacific coast. The species is believed to be solitary and to roost in tree cavities and rock crevices. It hunts high along forest edges and over ponds and clearings, flying rather slowly. As in many other species of bats, abrupt turning is achieved by extending and turning the broad side of the flight membrane of the wing in the direction of the turn, while the other wing performs a power stroke. Such turns can be executed very rapidly (1/16th of a second). Gentler turns are produced by a reduction of the braking effect on the side of the turn. Landing is achieved by using the flight membranes to brake. Aside from their primary function in flight, the wings and tail membrane also may be used in capturing insects. It consumes small flying insects. One baby is born in June or July. Status of populations are unknown, but it probably is uncommon.

Eastern Small-footed Bat

Myotis leibii

Weight is 3-5 grams (0.1-0.2 ounce), wingspan is 21-25 centimeters (8-10 inches), and distribution is from eastern Canada and New England south to Alabama and Georgia and west to Oklahoma. This is one of the smallest bats in the United States. Eastern small-footed bats hibernate in caves or mines and are among the hardiest of cave bats. They are one of the last to enter caves in autumn and often hibernate near cave or mine entrances where temperatures drop below freezing and where humidity is relatively low. Several have been found hibernating in cracks in cave floors and under rock slabs in quarries and elsewhere. The tolerance for cold, relatively dry places for hibernation is remarkable for such a small bat. In summer, they often inhabit buildings and caves; one small summer colony was behind a sliding door of a barn. They often fly repeated patterns within less than 1 meter (3 feet) of the floor of a cave or crevice, hang up on the wall, and then fly again. These bats emerge to forage shortly after sunset and fly slowly and erratically, usually 1-3 meters (3-10 feet) above the ground. Apparently these bats fill their stomachs within an hour after beginning to forage in the evening. They consume flies, mosquitos, true bugs, beetles, ants, and other insects. One baby is born in late spring or early summer. Nursery colonies of up to 20 bats have been reported from buildings. Lifespan is unknown but may be more than 9 years. It is uncommon throughout most of its range and is a species of special concern.

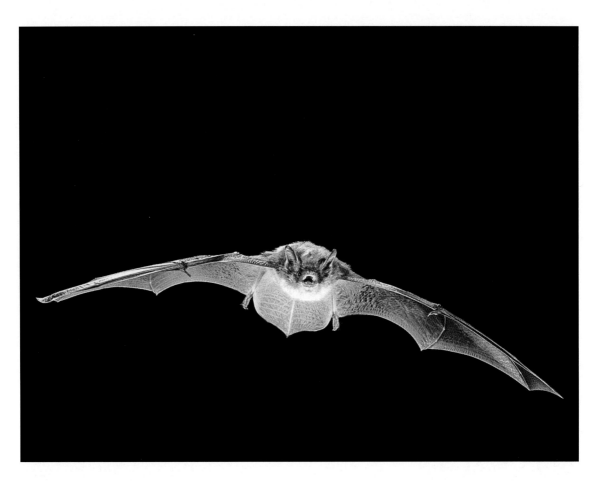

Little Brown Bat *Myotis lucifugus*

Weight is 7-14 grams (0.3-0.5 ounce), wingspan is 22-27 centimeters (9-11 inches), and this species is widely distributed from central Alaska to central Mexico. The little brown bat usually hibernates in caves and mines. During summer, it often inhabits buildings, usually rather hot attics, where females form nursery colonies of hundreds or even thousands of individuals. Where most males spend the summer is unknown, but they likely are solitary and scattered in a variety of roost types. Colonies usually are close to a lake or stream. This species seems to prefer to forage over water but also forages among trees in rather open areas. When foraging, it may repeat a set hunting pattern around houses or trees. It eats insects, including gnats, crane flies, beetles, wasps, and moths. Insects usually are captured with a wing tip, immediately transferred into a scoop formed by the forwardly curled tail and interfemoral membrane, and then grasped with the teeth. Mating occurs in autumn but also may occur during the hibernation period. One baby is born in May, June, or early July. When the mother is at rest during the day, she keeps the baby beneath a wing. Lifespan may be more than 20 years. This species is one of the most common bats throughout much of the northern United States and Canada but is scarce or only locally common in the southern part of its range. A subspecies found in the southwestern United States, *M. l. occultus* (Arizona bat), is considered to be of special concern.

Northern Long-eared Bat   *Myotis septentrionalis*

Weight is 6-9 grams (0.2-0.3 ounce), wingspan is 23-27 centimeters (9-11 inches), and distribution includes southern Canada and the central and eastern United States southward to northern Florida. Northern long-eared bats hibernate in parts of caves and mines that are relatively cool and moist, and where the air is still. Hibernation may begin as early as August and may last for 8-9 months in northern latitudes. In summer, they roost by day in a variety of shelters, including buildings and under tree bark and shutters, but at night they commonly use caves as night roosts. Northern long-eared bats seem much more solitary in their habits than other members of the genus *Myotis*, and they generally are found singly or in small groups containing up to 100 individuals. Although they frequently hang in the open, they seem to prefer tight crevices and holes. Sometimes only the nose and ears are visible, but they can be distinguished from most other species of *Myotis* by their long ears. These bats forage mainly on forested hillsides and ridges rather than in streamside and floodplain forests. They consume a variety of small night-flying insects. Presumably most mating occurs in autumn prior to hibernation. Apparently small nursery colonies are formed in June and July where pregnant females give birth to one baby. Mothers may be able to retrieve their young that fall from roost sites. Lifespan may be more than 18 years. This species is common over much of its range.

Indiana Bat   *Myotis sodalis*

Weight is 6-9 grams (0.2-0.3 ounce), wingspan is 24-28 centimeters (9-11 inches), and its distribution includes cave regions and, during summer, areas relatively near cave regions in the eastern United States. Indiana bats usually hibernate in large dense clusters of up to several thousand individuals in sections of the hibernation cave where temperatures average 3-6°C (38-43°F) and with relative humidities of 66-95%. They hibernate from October to April, depending on climactic conditions. Females depart hibernation caves before males and arrive at summer maternity roosts in mid-May. The summer roost of adult males often is near maternity roosts, but where most spend the day is unknown. Others remain near the hibernaculum, and a few males are found in caves during summer. Between early August and mid-September, Indiana bats arrive near their hibernation caves and engage in swarming and mating activity. Swarming at cave entrances continues into mid- or late October. During this time, fat reserves are built up for hibernation. When pregnant, females eat soft-bodied insects; they eat moths when lactating, and moths, beetles, and hard-bodied insects after lactation. Males also eat a variety of insects. One baby is born in June and is raised under loose tree bark, primarily in wooded-streamside habitat. Lifespans of nearly 14 years have been documented. The present total population of this endangered species is fewer than 360,000, with more than 85% hibernating at only nine locations, making them extremely vulnerable to destruction. Populations continue to decrease in spite of recovery efforts.

Fringed Bat *Myotis thysanodes*

Weight is 5-7 grams (0.2-0.3 ounce), wingspan is 27-32 centimeters (11-13 inches), and distribution includes southern British Columbia, Canada, western United States, and most of Mexico. The fringed bat occurs in a variety of habitats from desert-scrub to fir-pine associations. Oak and pinyon woodlands appear to be the most commonly used vegetative associations. Roost sites may be in caves, mines, and buildings. There are periodic changes in roost sites within a maternity roost because of thermoregulatory requirements of the bats; for example, clusters of bats move in response to temperature changes in different parts of the roost. Fringed bats are known to migrate, but little is known about the magnitude of movements. Females prepare physiologically for hibernation during the post-lactation period of late summer and early autumn, prior to migration. Individuals may awaken from hibernation periodically throughout winter. Diet includes beetles and moths. These bats forage close to the vegetative canopy and have relatively slow and highly maneuverable flight. Mating takes place in autumn. Ovulation, fertilization, and implantation occur in late April and early May, and one baby is born in late June or early July. Birth occurs in a head-down posture. After parturition, newborn bats are placed in a cluster separate from adults. Adults then fly to the cluster of newborn, suckle their baby, and return to their original roost site. This species is of special concern.

Cave Bat

Myotis velifer

Weight is 12-15 grams (0.4-0.5 ounce), wingspan is 28-33 centimeters (11-13 inches), and distribution is southern Kansas and western Oklahoma, the southwestern United States, Mexico, and into Central America. This bat occurs in colonies of 2,000-5,000 individuals throughout much of its range. Habitats vary from desert floodplains and rocky canyonlands to the cave country from central Texas to southcentral Kansas. In summer, this species congregates in caves, mines, and less often in buildings. Most individuals in populations in Arizona and California appear to be migratory, and most in Kansas, Oklahoma, and Texas appear to be permanent residents that hibernate in caves during winter. Flight is stronger, more direct, and with less flutter than most other bats of the genus. These bats begin emerging from the daytime roost well before dark, fill their stomachs within about 0.5 hour of foraging, and retire to some shelter such as a building, cave, or mine for a night resting period. There is no clearly defined second foraging period in early morning as in some other species. Predators include snakes, hawks, owls, and raccoons. Like many insectivorous bats, this species is opportunistic in feeding habits, with diets that fluctuate by season and habitat. Common food items are small moths and beetles. After a gestation of 60-70 days, one baby is born in late June or early July. During parturition (20 minutes), the baby is caught in the mother's folded tail membrane, and then it crawls to a nipple and begins to nurse. Lifespan may be 10-12 years. This species is of special concern.

48

Long-legged Bat

Myotis volans

Weight is 6-9 grams (0.2-0.3 ounce), wingspan is 25-30 centimeters (10-12 inches), and distribution is southern Alaska and western Canada southward into northern Mexico. The long-legged bat primarily inhabits forested mountain regions, where it roosts in trees, rock crevices, cracks and crevices in stream banks, and in buildings. It also may be found in streamside and arid habitats in some areas. This bat emerges early in the evening when it is still twilight, and it is a rapid, direct flier that pursues prey over relatively long distances through, around, and over the forest canopy. This species is active throughout most of the night, although there is a peak of activity in the first 3-4 hours after sunset. It is moderately gregarious in maternity colonies and during swarming in late summer and hibernation. Hibernation sites include caves and mine tunnels. There usually are more males than females at hibernation sites. The ability to fly at cool temperatures may enable this species to extend the prehibernation period of activity. The long-legged bat feeds primarily on moths, although it also consumes other, primarily soft-bodied invertebrates, including flies, termites, lacewings, wasps, true bugs, leafhoppers, and small beetles. One baby is born in July. Maternity colonies may be in crevices in rocks, trees, stream banks, or in buildings. Lifespan may be up to 21 years. This species is of special concern.

Yuma Bat   *Myotis yumanensis*

Weight is 4-6 grams (0.1-0.2 ounce), wingspan is 22-26 centimeters (9-10 inches), and distribution is from southwestern British Columbia, through the western United States, and into central Mexico. From the cottonwood-lined streams of the desert Southwest to the redwood canyons of the Pacific coast, nearly all habitats of the Yuma bat show a common feature, the presence of open water nearby. It often is found in areas without trees. Although locally abundant, the species seems to be absent in many apparently suitable feeding areas. The Yuma bat emerges when it is nearly dark and forages just above the surface of streams and ponds. Night roosts often show little or no evidence of use, but careful searching of abandoned cabins, attics, porches, and similar sites usually will reveal guano. In late May and early June, large nursery colonies may form in buildings, caves, mines, and under bridges. As with many other bats, males take no part in care of the young and usually are not found near nursery roosts. Instead, adult males usually scatter and lead somewhat solitary lifestyles. Nursery roosts are quickly abandoned if disturbed. The nursery roosts are vacated in autumn, although the migrational destination of the bats is unknown. Diet includes beetles and relatively soft-bodied insects such as flies, termites, moths, and mayflies. One baby is born in late May or in June. Females give birth for the first time in the summer following their own birth. This species is of special concern.

Evening Bat   *Nycticeius humeralis*

Weight is 7-14 grams (0.3-0.5 ounce), wingspan is 26-29 centimeters (10-11 inches), and distribution is southern Ontario, Canada, most of the eastern United States, and northeastern Mexico. This species usually inhabits tree cavities or buildings in summer. In the Southeast, it may share roosts with the Brazilian free-tailed bat. It almost never enters caves, although it sometimes joins the bats swarming about certain entrances in late summer. Maternity colonies in buildings sometimes contain hundreds of individuals. Smaller colonies may occur behind the loose bark of dead pines and in hollow cypress trees. Winter habitat is almost completely unknown, but evening bats accumulate large reserves of fat in autumn, sufficient for either hibernation or a long migration. This species emerges early and flies a slow and steady course. Heavy rain and cold temperatures retard activity, and females nursing young return to the roost periodically to care for their offspring. It consumes a variety of small insects. Babies are born in nursery roosts sometime between mid-May and mid-June. The usual litter size is two. As with most other species of bats, birth is by breech presentation. After the babies are born, they grasp a nipple within 5-8 minutes. Newborns are pink, except for slightly darker feet, membranes, ears, and lips; their skin is so transparent the viscera can be seen. Lifespan is greater than 5 years. Although less common through most of its range, it is one of the most common bats throughout the southern-coastal states.

Western Pipistrelle Bat   *Pipistrellus hesperus*

Weight is 3-6 grams (0.1-0.2 ounce), wingspan is 19-23 centimeters (7-9 inches), and distribution is from southern Washington to southern Mexico. The western pipistrelle bat is one of the smallest bats in the United States. Primarily a desert species, it inhabits a variety of habitats from rocky canyons, cliffs, and outcroppings to creosotebush flats. Day roosts usually are in rock crevices, but may be beneath rocks, in burrows, in mines, and in buildings. It tends to roost singly or in small groups; a maternity colony of 12 individuals is the largest known group of this species. In winter, it has been found hibernating in mines, caves, and rock crevices. Among the most diurnal of bats, it often begins foraging flights before sunset and may remain active well after dawn. However, except for lactating females that may be active throughout the night, early evening activity usually ceases within 1-2 hours after sunset. The flight is fluttery and is among the slowest and weakest of all our bats. A slight breeze can bring these bats to a standstill, and a stronger wind may cause them to seek shelter. This bat forages 2-25 meters (7-82 feet) above ground on swarming insects, and consumes about 20% of its body weight per feeding. Prey items include caddisflies, stoneflies, moths, small beetles, leaf and stilt bugs, leafhoppers, flies, mosquitos, ants, and wasps. Twins are born in June or July, after a gestation of about 40 days. Newborn bats weigh less than 1 gram, but they grow quickly. Juveniles begin to fly at about 1 month of age. It is relatively common throughout most of its range.

Eastern Pipistrelle Bat　　　　　*Pipistrellus subflavus*

Weight is 6-8 grams (0.2-0.3 ounce), wingspan is 21-26 centimeters (8-10 inches), and distribution includes eastern Canada, most of the eastern United States, and southward through eastern Mexico to Central America. Caves, mines, and rock crevices are used as hibernation sites in winter, and occasionally as night roosts in summer. These bats rarely occur in buildings, and apparently most roost in trees in summer. This species inhabits more caves in eastern North America than any other species of bat, usually hanging singly in warmer parts of the cave. An individual may occupy a precise spot in a cave on consecutive winters; it usually has several spots in which it hangs, shifting from one to another during the winter. This bat emerges from its daytime retreat early in the evening. It is a weak flier and so small that it may be mistaken for a large moth. Eastern pipistrelle bats usually are solitary, although occasionally in late summer four or five will appear about a single tree. The flight is erratic, and the foraging area is small. It often forages over waterways and forest edges and eats moths, beetles, mosquitos, true bugs, ants, and other insects. Mating occurs in autumn, sperm are stored during winter, and fertilization takes place in spring. These bats usually bear twins in late spring or early summer. Babies are born hairless and pink with eyes closed, and they are capable of making clicking sounds that may aid their mothers in locating them. They grow rapidly and can fly within a month. This species is common throughout its range.

Rafinesque's Big-eared Bat   *Corynorhinus rafinesquii*

Weight is 8-14 grams (0.3-0.5 ounce), wingspan is 26-30 centimeters (10-12 inches), and distribution is the southeastern United States. This species is one of the least known of all bats in the eastern United States. In the northern part of its range, it hibernates in caves, mines, or similar habitats, including cisterns and wells. In contrast, Rafinesque's big-eared bats usually are not found in caves during winter in the more southern parts of their range. Maternity colonies usually are found in abandoned buildings, sometimes in rather well-lighted areas. They usually consist of few to several dozen adults. Maternity colonies are found more rarely in caves and mines. Males generally are solitary during summer, roosting in buildings or hollow trees. When approached in summer, these bats are immediately alerted and begin to wave their ears, apparently trying to keep track of the intruder. This species and the eastern pipistrelle bat choose more open and lighted day roosts than other kinds of bats. Both species commonly hang in the open in plain sight. Rafinesque's big-eared bats emerge late in the evening to forage; apparently it does not forage at twilight. Its flight is remarkably agile. Moths and other night-flying insects are eaten. One baby is born in late May or early June in the northern part of the range and about mid-May in the South. The young shed their milk teeth in mid-July and reach adult size by August or early September. This species is uncommon over most of its range and is of special concern.

Townsend's Big-eared Bat   *Corynorhinus townsendii*

Weight is 8-14 grams (0.3-0.5 ounce), wingspan is 30-34 centimeters (12-13 inches), and distribution includes western Canada, the western United States to southern Mexico, and a few isolated populations in the eastern United States. These bats hibernate in caves or mines where the temperature is 12°C (54°F) or less, but usually above freezing. Hibernation sites in caves often are near entrances in well-ventilated areas. If temperatures near entrances become extreme, they move to more thermally stable parts of the cave. They hibernate in clusters of a few to more than 100 individuals. During hibernation, the long ears may be erect or coiled. Solitary bats sometimes hang by only one foot. Maternity colonies usually are located in relatively warm parts of caves. During the maternity period, males apparently are solitary. Where most males spend the summer is unknown. No long-distance migrations are known. Like many other bats, they return year after year to the same roost sites. It is believed to feed entirely on moths. Mating begins in autumn and continues into winter, sperm are stored during winter, and fertilization occurs shortly after arousal from hibernation. One baby is born in June. Babies are large at birth, weighing nearly 25% as much as their mother. They can fly in 2.5-3 weeks and are weaned by 6 weeks. Lifespan may be 16 or more years. The two subspecies in the eastern United States, *C. t. virginianus* (Virginia big-eared bat) and *C. t. ingens* (Ozark big-eared bat) are considered endangered. Two western subspecies, *C. t. townsendii* (Townsend's big-eared bat) and *C. t. pallescens* (Western big-eared bat) are of special concern.

Wagner's Mastiff Bat   *Eumops glaucinus*

Weight is 30-47 grams (1.1-1.7 ounces), wingspan is 49-53 centimeters (19-21 inches), and, within the United States, Wagner's mastiff bat occurs only in southern Florida. Elsewhere, the distribution extends from central and western Mexico southward through northern South America. It also occurs in Cuba and Jamaica. Although these bats are known to occur in cities as well as in forested areas, precise foraging and roosting habits and long-term requirements are unknown. In Florida, favorite daytime roosts are under the shingles of Spanish-tile roofs, but some have been found in shafts of leaves of royal palms, in low shrubbery, in places where there are lush growths of tropical flowers and shrubs, and one colony was in a cavity in a longleaf pine. At any time during the year, juveniles, adult males, and adult females may occur in the same roost. Unlike most other free-tailed bats, which need to drop 8-10 meters (26-33 feet) from a roost before they can fly, Wagner's mastiff bat can take flight from horizontal surfaces. These bats leave their roost after dark and seldom fly below 10 meters (33 feet). Their loud, piercing calls can be heard for some distance, and once a person recognizes this call, it can easily be differentiated from other nighttime sounds. They do not migrate. The diet includes beetles, flies, mosquitos, true bugs, moths, and other insects. One baby is born in June, July, August, or September. It is rare in the United States and the subspecies found there, *E. g. floridanus* (Florida mastiff bat) is of special concern.

Greater Mastiff Bat

Eumops perotis

Weight is 60-70 grams (2.1-2.5 ounces), wingspan is 53-58 centimeters (21-23 inches), and distribution is central California to central Mexico and northern South America to northern Argentina. It is capable of fast and prolonged flight; the wings are long and slender and the flight membranes are tough and leathery. These bats live in high, dry places, and usually cannot get airborne from the ground, but will scramble to a post or a tree to gain height for launching. In the southwestern United States, the greater mastiff bat is most common in rugged rocky canyons and cliffs, where crevices provide favored daytime retreats. Colonies are small, usually less than 100, and adult males sometimes are found in maternity colonies. Some roost sites are occupied throughout the year, but the four seasons usually are spent in different roosts. This species produces a high-pitched call that can be heard when they are flying up to 300 meters (990 feet) above ground. Males have a dermal gland that becomes enlarged during the mating season. When enlarged, this gland produces a thick, oily secretion with a strong odor that may serve to attract females. It feeds on insects, including dragonflies, grasshoppers, beetles, true bugs, moths, wasps, and ants. Mating occurs in early spring when the dermal gland of the male is most functional. Parturition dates usually vary more in this species than in any other bat in the United States; May to September. One baby ordinarily is born; twins are rare. The subspecies found in the United States, *E. p. californicus* (western mastiff bat), is of special concern.

Underwood's Mastiff Bat *Eumops underwoodi*

Weight is 50-60 grams (1.8-2.1 ounces), wingspan is 50-55 centimeters (20-22 inches), and distribution is in southcentral Arizona, then along the western coast of Mexico into Central America. Among bats of the United States, this species is second in size only to the greater mastiff bat. Its long, narrow wings are adapted for rapid, long-distance flight in open habitats. The flight speed is at least 43 kilometers per hour (26 miles per hour). As in other free-tailed bats, the distal part of the tail is not attached to the interfemoral membrane. It is known in the United States only from the vicinity of the Baboquivari Mountains, Arizona. Information on habitat of this species in the United States is scarce (we only know that it may fly over livestock watering tanks in the mesquite desert of southern Arizona), and its distribution in winter is unknown. However, it occurs in a variety of habitats in Mexico and Central America, including arid lowlands, grasslands, and pine-oak and deciduous forests; one was present during the day beneath a leaf of a royal palm. Roosts are in high, dry places; one roost was in a large, hollow tree. Its presence can be detected by listening for the high-pitched "peeps" emitted several times a minute in flight. The calls may be intense enough to hurt the ears of anyone standing close by when these bats are flying. This insectivorous bat consumes grasshoppers, leafhoppers, moths, and a variety of beetles. One baby is born in late June or in July. It is rare in the United States and is of special concern.

Pallas' Mastiff Bat   *Molossus molossus*

Weight is 13-15 grams (0.5 ounce), wingspan is 29-33 centimeters (11-13 inches), and this species is widely distributed from northern Mexico and from the Florida Keys southward through the Caribbean and northern South America to northern Argentina. Throughout its broad range from the Florida Keys through Central America and most of South America, this species commonly is associated with human dwellings, but it also roosts in hollow trees, crevices in rocks, caves, tunnels, culverts, and bridges. Females form nursery colonies at the beginning of the rainy season in buildings, hollow trees, or caves. Individuals also have been known to roost in palm fronds. The three colonies known in the Florida Keys are all in the roof spaces of flat-roofed buildings. Temperatures in roosts of this species may reach 55°C (131°F). These bats fly rapidly in the manner of swifts. Pallas' mastiff bat forages near streams in dry deciduous forest and moist-tropical evergreen forest. In drier areas, it often forages near man-made ponds. This mastiff bat eats insects including moths, beetles, and flying ants. One baby is born in June-September. Mothers leave their baby in clusters of other babies when they go to forage. Upon returning, mothers identify their baby by its calls. Lactation lasts about 6 weeks; weaning occurs at about 65 days of age. Rare in the United States, this species is known only from the Florida Keys. However, throughout most of its range, Pallas' mastiff bat is common.

Pocketed Free-tailed Bat　　　*Nyctinomops femorosaccus*

Weight is 10-14 grams (0.4-0.5 ounce), wingspan is 34-37 centimeters (13-15 inches), and distribution is from the southwestern United States to southcentral Mexico. The common and scientific names refer to a shallow fold of skin on the underside of the interfemoral membrane near the knee, which forms a pocket-like structure. It occurs in the arid low-lands of the desert Southwest, and primarily roosts in crevices in rugged cliffs, slopes, and tall rocky outcrops. Colonies are small, usually less than 100 individuals. In day roosts, these bats squeak or chatter much of the time and usually will leave the roost well after dark. When first taking flight, they produce shrill, sharp, high-pitched chattering calls, which may continue while the bats are in flight. As with other free-tailed bats, the flight is swift and lacks the fluttering characteristic of many other bats. At stock ponds and other water sources, they fly swiftly about the pool, making distinctly audible whistling and fluttering sounds with their wings. In drinking, these bats will hit the water hard while in flight and scoop up a mouthful of water. Moths are common prey, but other foods include beetles, flying ants, flies, leafhoppers, crickets, stinkbugs, lacewings, and grasshoppers. One baby is born in late June or July. This species is uncommon in the United States.

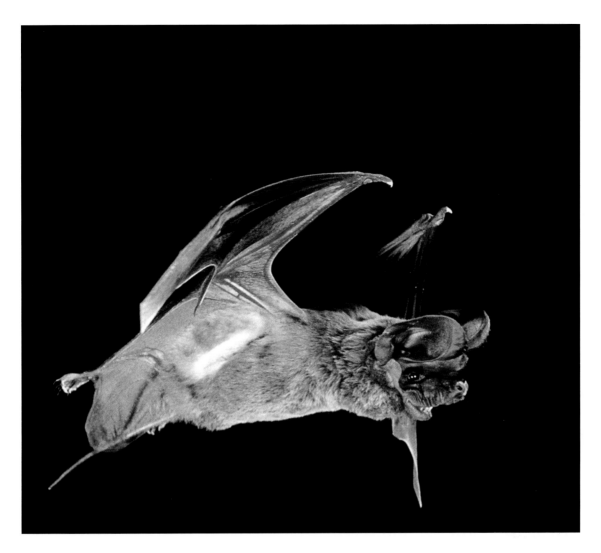

Big Free-tailed Bat   *Nyctinomops macrotis*

Weight is 25-30 grams (0.9-1.1 ounces), wingspan is 42-46 centimeters (17-18 inches), and distribution is in the southwestern United States, Caribbean, and Central America through northern South America. The big free-tailed bat inhabits rocky country, where it roosts in crevices high up on cliff faces, but it has been known to roost in buildings. This bat leaves its roost late, when it is quite dark. As the species is incapable of hibernation, the northern populations are believed to be migratory. In Utah, the northern part of the distributional range of the species, individuals are present from the latter one-half of May to mid-September, but none are present in winter. This bat is a fast and powerful flier, and after the young are weaned, individuals may appear hundreds of kilometers beyond what seems to be the usual range. Records of accidental occurrence are widespread in North America; for example, there are autumn records from Iowa and British Columbia. When foraging, the big free-tailed bat usually emits a loud piercing chatter. Parasites include bat bugs and fleas. Diet consists primarily of large moths but may include crickets, flying ants, stinkbugs, and leafhoppers. Maternity colonies are formed by females, who give birth to one baby in June or July. It is uncommon throughout most of its range and is of special concern.

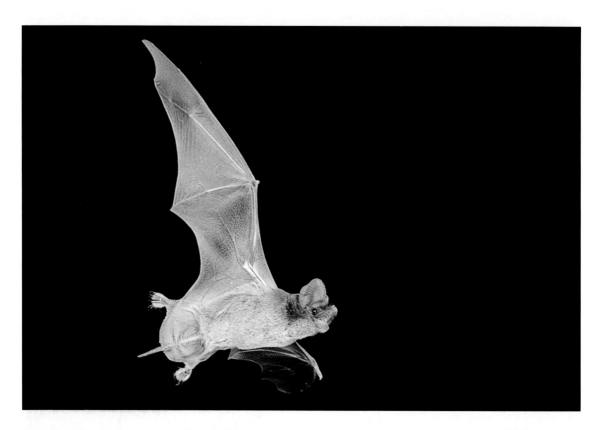

Brazilian Free-tailed Bat

Tadarida brasiliensis

Weight is 11-15 grams (0.4-0.5 ounce), wingspan is 30-35 centimeters (12-14 inches), and distribution is in the southern United States and southward through Mexico and Central America into northern South America. It also occurs on islands of the Caribbean. Habitat of Brazilian free-tailed bats differs in various parts of the United States. In the Southwest, they primarily are cave bats that migrate long distances into Mexico to winter. During summer, about 20,000,000 bats of this species occupy Bracken Cave near San Antonio, Texas; this is the largest concentration of mammals in the world. In the Southeast, this species does not occur in caves; it is present only in man-made structures. It does not migrate great distances (if at all), and few colonies larger than a few hundred individuals are known. They often select hot attics and caves as roosts; babies seem to be able to tolerate higher temperatures than adults. High temperatures in roosts are essential for rapid growth of young bats; apparently, the larger the colony, the less the energy expenditure per bat to maintain a given temperature. This species usually feeds on small moths and beetles. One baby is born in late spring or early summer. Birth occurs with the mother hanging head downward. Passage of the baby through the birth canal requires about 90 seconds. Newborns are hairless, but have all their milk teeth. Mothers can locate their own baby among the thousands of babies in a colony. The subspecies inhabiting the southwestern United States in summer is referred to as the Mexican free-tailed bat and is present in very large numbers. It has been estimated that more than 100,000,000 are present in Texas alone during summer. The subspecies found in the southeastern United States, LeConte's free-tailed bat, is only locally common.

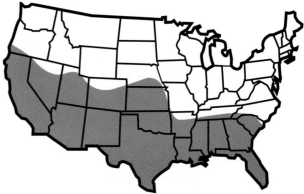

Summary

Bats comprise an extremely interesting and highly beneficial segment of our fauna. They should be understood and appreciated, not feared and persecuted. Like many wild animals, they sometimes pose public health problems or become nuisances by residing where they are not wanted. However, their benefit as the only major predators of night-flying insects greatly outweighs their negative aspects.

Although only seven U.S. bats (four entire species and three subspecies) are listed as endangered, most species seem to be steadily declining in number, some at a rapid rate. Human disturbance to hibernating and maternity colonies and the all too prevalent attitude that "the only good bat is a dead bat" have been important factors in declining bat populations. Habitat destruction and the use of pesticides and other chemical toxicants have no doubt also taken a heavy toll, not only of bats, but of many other fascinating and beneficial species as well.

The steady decline in populations of bats, as well as that of many other species, represents much more than just a decrease in a population of organisms. It also reflects a steady decline in our overall quality of life.

Fish-eating bats (Noctilio leporinus) of Mexico, Central America, and South America catch fish by skimming over water and gaffing fish with their long claws.

Books About Bats

Books for Older Students

Altringham, J. D. 1996. Bats: Biology and Behavior. Oxford University Press, Inc., Oxford, United Kingdom, 262 pp.

Barbour, R. W., and W. H. Davis. 1969. Bats of America. University Press of Kentucky, Lexington, 286 pp.

Fenton, M. B. 1992. Bats. Facts on File, New York, 207 pp.

Hill, J. E., and J. D. Smith. 1984. Bats: A Natural History. University of Texas Press, Austin, 250 pp.

Kunz, T. H. (ed.). 1982. Ecology of Bats. Plenum Publishing Corporation, New York, 444 pp.

Nowak, R. M. 1994. Walker's Bats of the World. The Johns Hopkins University Press, Baltimore, Maryland, 240 pp.

Tuttle, M. D. 1988. America's Neighborhood Bats. University of Texas Press, Austin, 96 pp.

Tuttle, M. D., and D. L. Hensley. 1993. The Bat House Builder's Handbook. Bat Conservation International, Austin, Texas, 34 pp.

Books for Younger Students

Arnold, C. 1996. Bat. Morrow Junior Books, New York, 48 pp.

Bash, B. 1993. Shadows of the Night: The Hidden World of the Little Brown Bat. Sierra Club Books for Children, San Francisco, California, 30 pp.

Cannon, J. 1993. Stellaluna. Harcourt Brace and Company, New York, 48 pp.

Lollar, A. 1992. The Bat in My Pocket: A Memorable Friendship. Capra Press, Santa Barbara, California, 86 pp.

Lovett, S. 1991. Extremely Weird Bats. John Muir Publications, Santa Fe, New Mexico, 50 pp.

Milton, J. 1993. Bats: Creatures of the Night. Grosset and Dunlap, Inc., New York, 48 pp.

Rink, D., and L. C. Wood. 1989. Bats. Zoobooks. Wildlife Education Ltd., San Diego, California, 17 pp.

Stuart, D. 1994. Bats: Mysterious Flyers of the Night. Carolrhoda Books, Inc., Minneapolis, Minnesota, 45 pp.

These and other books about bats are available from Bat Conservation International, P.O. Box 162603, Austin, TX 78716-2603 (800/538-BATS).